D1383352

It's Time!

By Julie Pepper   Illustrated by Anne Steele

It's Time

Copyright © 2016 By Julie Pepper

Artwork Copyright © 2016 By Anne Steele

All rights reserved. No part of this book may be reproduced in any form or by any electronic or mechanical means including information storage and retrieval systems – except in the case of brief quotations embodied in critical articles or reviews – without permission in writing from its publisher, Clear Fork Publishing.

Summary:It's Time welcomes you to share in the preparation for the very first day of school through the eyes of a child. This near-wordless picture book will draw you into a little boy's perception of his moments at home that lead him to his new school, teacher, and class. See what he sees as he is awaken by his mom, and goes through the steps of getting ready for his big day. A connection is made that will open a whole new world for this little one.

Clear Fork Publishing
P.O. Box 870
102 S. Swenson
Stamford, Texas 79553
(325)773-5550
www.clearforkpublishing.com

Printed and Bound in the United States of America.

ISBN - 978-1-946101-27-3
LCN - 2017946099

www.clearforkpublishing.com

To Teacher "Hana" and Teacher Ann. Thank you for supporting, teaching, inspiring, and loving my wee ones. You were their first teachers outside of our home, and I am forever grateful! - Julie

Dedicated to my father, John Steele who always believed in my crazy dreams and to every child at heart. Keep your eyes wide and your heart open and nothing is impossible. Art is everywhere and in everything. - Anne

It's time to
wake up!

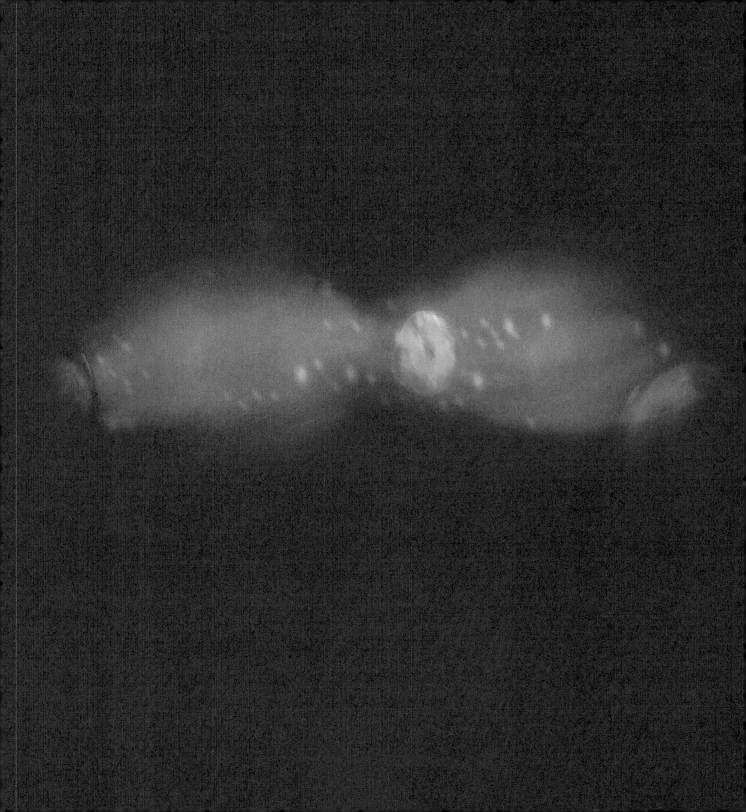

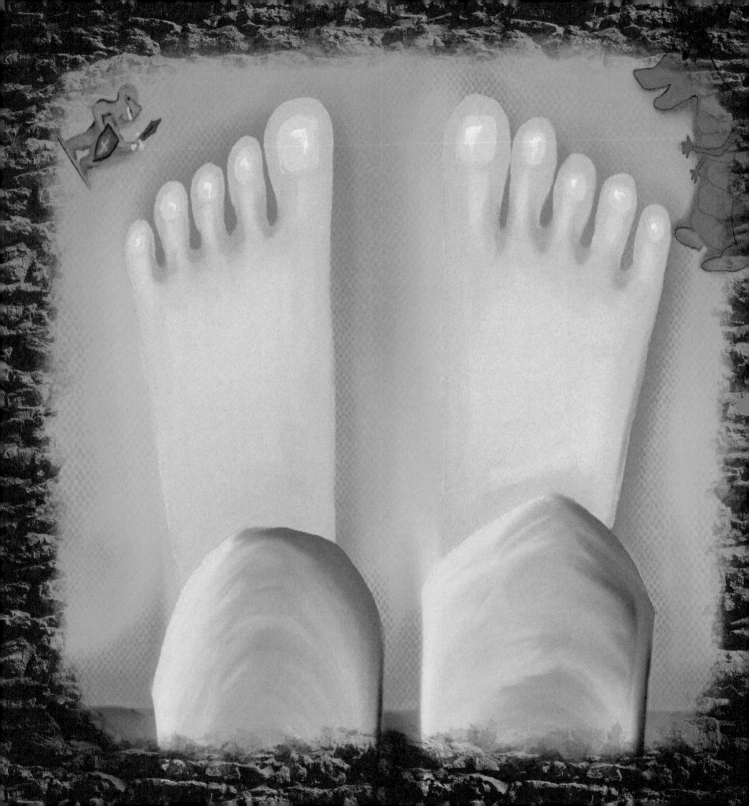

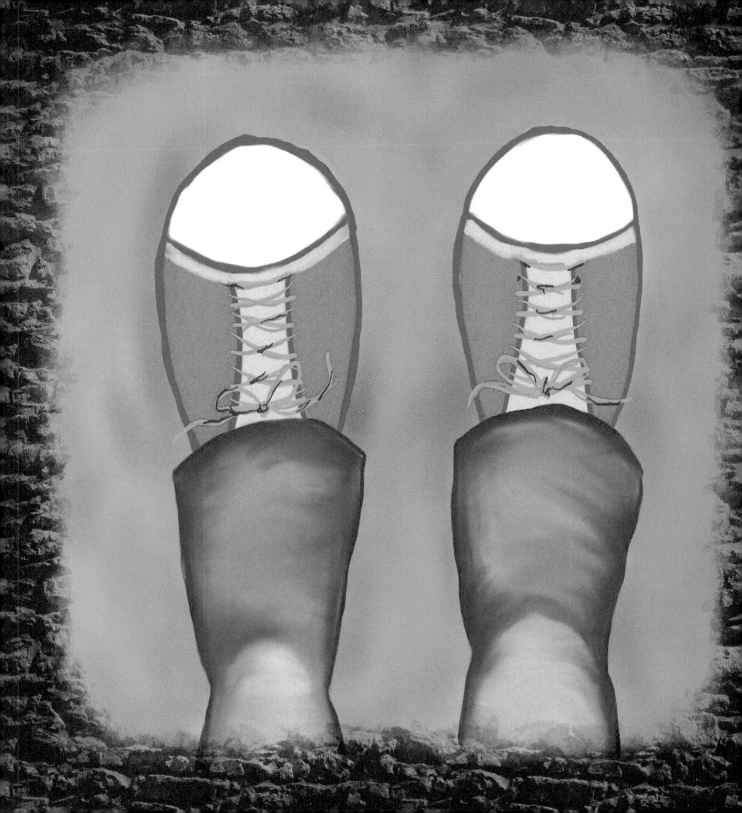

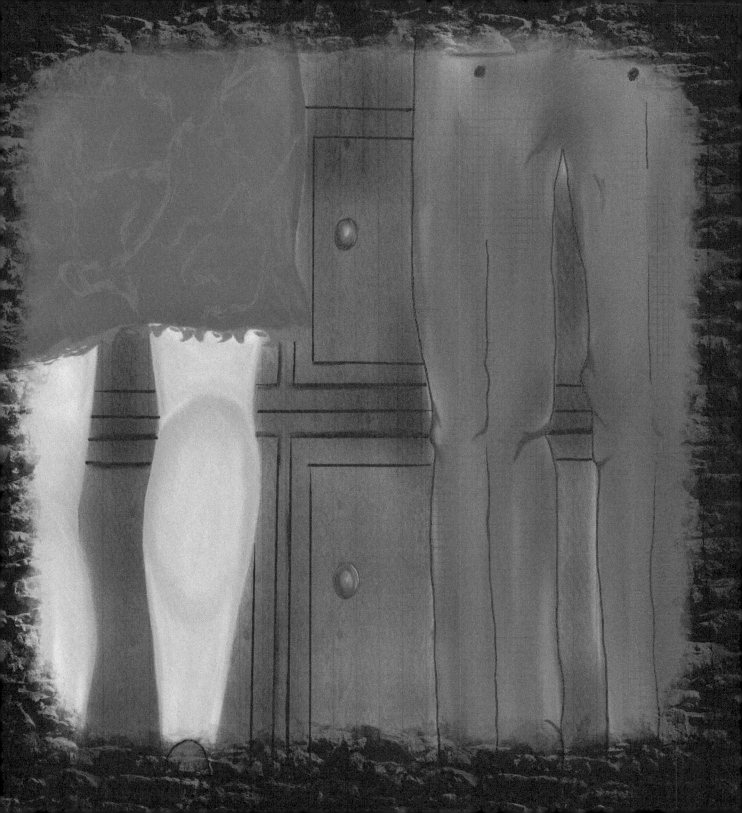

It's time to go!

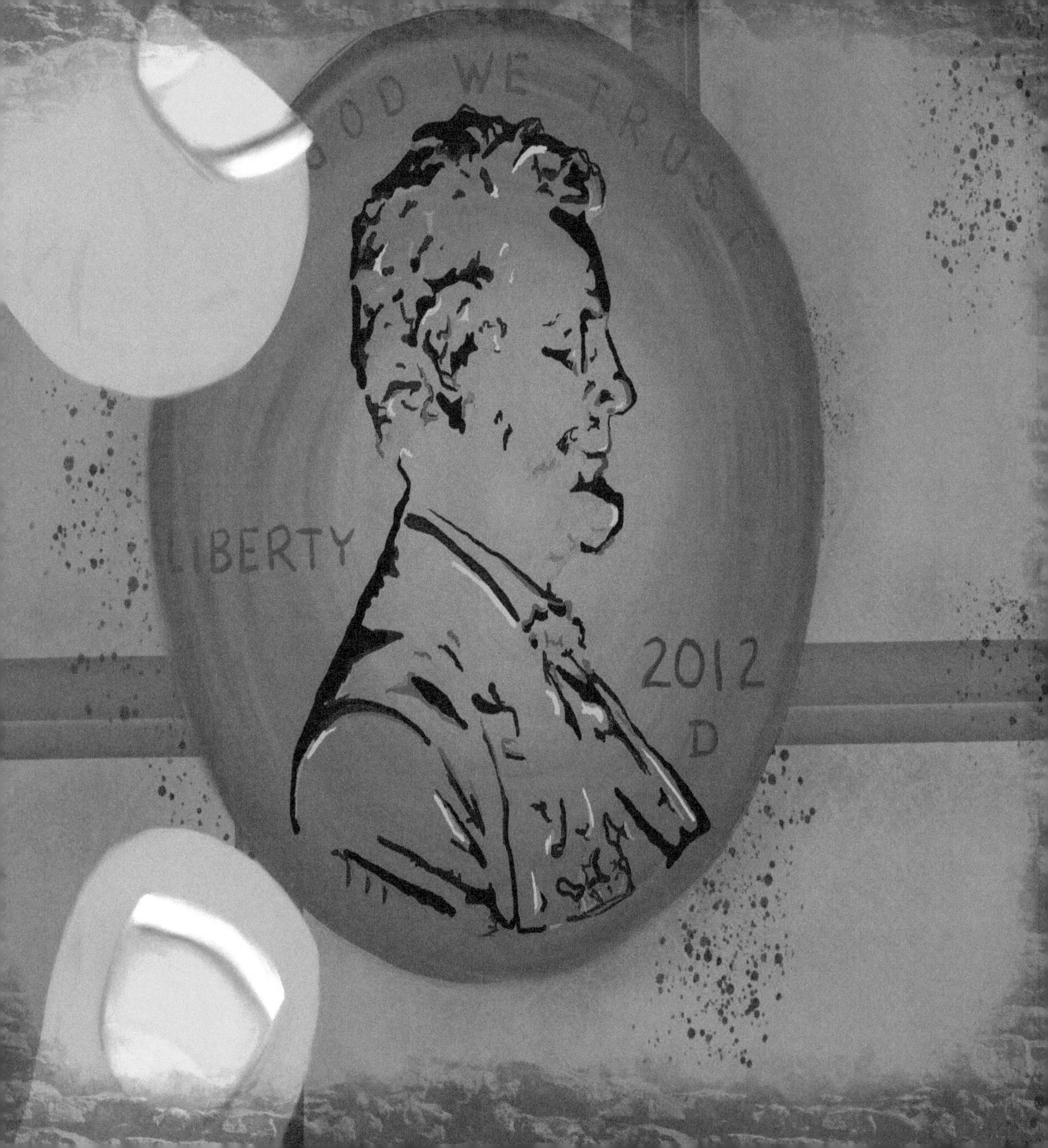
GOD WE TRUST
LIBERTY
2012
D

THE WHOLE WORLD OPENED TO ME
WHEN I LEARNED TO READ.
~MARY MCLEOD BETHUNE

Welcome!
It's time to have a great day!

red
orange
yellow
green
blue
indigo
violet
brown

Julie Pepper grew up in the foothills of California in Amador County. She attended UC Davis as an undergraduate where she wrote the humor column, *Pepp Talk*. During her time there, she also studied Shakespeare abroad in England and Italy. After college she worked in marketing and sales before realizing a true passion for teaching. Julie is now a National Board Certified teacher who holds an M.A.Ed. with an emphasis in Arts in Education. She has been teaching 5th grade in Northern California for ten years, and uses picture books to teach reading and writing mini-lessons. Julie currently lives in Davis, California with her husband and their three hilarious children.

Anne Steele grew up in the foothills of Amador County. Ever since she could hold a pencil or stand on a stage, she embraced all things creative. Throughout school, she was always active in theater and art which led her to having a diploma in Baking and Pastry as well as an AA in Art History. Her career path has led her into a life of fun and creativity. Anne currently lives in Portland, OR enjoying the culture and creating art!

CPSIA information can be obtained
at www.ICGtesting.com
Printed in the USA
BVOW05*1445311017
498656BV00015B/36/P

9 781946 101273